ARCHIMEDES &
THE FULCRUM
The Big Idea
PAUL STRATHERN

arrow books

Reissued by Arrow Books 2010

1 3 5 7 9 10 8 6 4 2

Copyright © Paul Strathern, 1998

Paul Strathern has asserted his right under the Copyright,
Designs and Patents Act, 1988, to be identified as
the author of this work.

First published in Great Britain in 1998 by Arrow Books

The Random House Group Limited
20 Vauxhall Bridge Road, London, SW1V 2SA

www.rbooks.co.uk

Addresses for companies within The Random House Group
Limited can be found at:
www.randomhouse.co.uk/offices.htm

The Random House Group Limited Reg. No. 954009

A CIP catalogue record for this book
is available from the British Library

ISBN 9780099238126

The Random House Group Limited supports The Forest
Stewardship Council (FSC), the leading international forest
certification organisation. All our titles that are printed on
Greenpeace approved FSC certified paper carry the FSC
logo. Our paper procurement policy can be found at:
www.rbooks.co.uk/environment

Typeset by SX Composing DTP, Rayleigh, Essex

Printed and bound in Great Britain by
CPI Cox & Wyman, Reading, RG1 8EX

CONTENTS

Introduction 7

The World as Archimedes
Found It 9

The Life & Works of Archimedes 16

Afterword 75

Archimedes at Work 79

Chronology 85

Suggestions for Further Reading 88

INTRODUCTION

Archimedes was one of the three supreme mathematicians of all time – Newton and Gauss being generally accepted as his only peers. We all know the story about him jumping out of the bath shouting 'Eureka!' Almost as well known is his boast: 'Give me a place to stand and I can move the earth.' This refers to the fulcrum and his knowledge of levers, but in a way it refers to much, much more. Archimedes did indeed move the world. He shifted our entire view of it. The ancient Greeks transformed early mathematics and Archimedes had a supreme role in this – bringing the subject to the threshold of modern mathematical thinking. Where to all intents and purposes it languished for nearly two millennia. Sadly, the baton which Archimedes held out had no taker.

Archimedes' scientific thinking was part and

parcel of his mathematics. He revolutionized mechanics, invented hydrostatics, and established the precise study of more complex solids. The mathematics involved caused him to invent an early form of calculus, and brought him to an advanced understanding of arithmetic relations. He also excelled in the practical sphere. Pulleys and levers, a water pump, an early form of laser: these were amongst his inventions. And there may well have been more – which he either didn't bother to record, or which vanished forever with his lost works. Archimedes didn't rate his practical work, seldom bothering to record it. Yet the surviving treatises which do record his work remain as astonishing and as lucid as the day they were written. Happily most of them are also easy to follow, even for non-mathematicians. These works give a unique insight into the workings of a unique mind.

But even such a mind as Archimedes' does not spring out of nothing. To understand what he understood, and to appreciate what he did with this knowledge, it is first necessary to see what the world was like before he arrived on the scene.

THE WORLD AS
ARCHIMEDES FOUND IT

Science has its roots in rule-of-thumb learning. Indeed, such learning is even noticeable in creatures which don't possess thumbs. The cat's patient waiting at the entrance to the mousehole is scientific practice. There is a pattern of events here, which it expects to be repeated. (Meanwhile the mouse, leaving by another hole, is following its own scientific path.)

Causation (linking cause and effect), induction (inferring a general law from particular instances), and ordering (discerning physical and temporal patterns) – such are the basic scientific impulses. Science is the search for practical meaning ie, an explanation that can be *used*. This has been the basis of human science from pre-historic times until the first part of the 20th century. (Certain aspects of quantum theory and cosmology no longer conform to these scientific norms.)

Twentieth century science has changed everything, but similar significant advances have taken place in previous eras. One of these occurred around 2500 BC, when Stonehenge was erected in Britain and the Great Pyramid was built in Egypt. Both of these monuments incorporated religious and astronomical ideas whose sophistication was not fully appreciated until this century. Close investigation of Stonehenge and the pyramids revealed startling mathematical knowledge. The people who built both these monuments understood in the simplest practical terms the relationship between the two sides and the hypotenuse of certain right-angled triangles (ie, $a^2 + b^2 = c^2$). In other words, they had grasped the basis of what we know as Pythagoras' Theorem around 2,000 years before Pythagoras was born.

The main source of scientific and mathematical inspiration for both the ancient Egyptians and megalithic Britons lay in the heavens. The happenings in these upper realms were viewed with awe. Events here presaged both fine summer harvests and disasters. Here lay order, regularity, inflexible certainty.

This was understood contemporaneously in

India and China, Mesapotamia and Egypt, as well as in the Americas. These civilizations had few other similarities and in some cases no contact whatsoever at this time – suggesting that astronomy may have provided a kind of evolutionary trigger. Such a trigger process has been proposed to account for the many unexplained 'jumps' which have occurred, and continue to occur, in evolution ranging from primitive cells to human and dolphin genius.

Astronomy came of age around 2500 BC, and was to remain the 'queen of the sciences' for the next four millennia. (Echoes of this long reign remain in modern attitudes towards both astrological whimsy and the 'wonders' of modern cosmology.) Another evolutionary 'jump' for humanity occurred between the sixth and fourth centuries BC. This saw the sudden rise of ancient Greece, Confucianism and Taoism both founded in China, and Buddhism established in India.

By far the most intellectually significant of these events was the rise of ancient Greece. Its cultural legacy was western civilization. This was also where science, as we have come to understand it, began. So what happened? Science became separated from religion. Astronomy shed astrology. Reason, rather than intuition, held sway. Explanations of how the world worked were now backed by evidence, rather than religion, superstition or fairy tales. Proof was introduced into mathematics. Theorems replaced habitual procedure. Rules and laws were derived from the study of natural phenomena.

The reason why Pythagoras' Theorem is named after him is because he was the first to *prove* it. The Greeks continued to believe in the gods, but from now on divine behaviour was subject to the restraints of reason. (Apart, of course, from miracles – which were only allowed to take place in the absence of scientific observers.)

Pythagoras even went one further. According to him, the world was bound to behave in a mathematical fashion. He was the first to say this, back in the fourth century BC, and we still believe it. Though not for the same reason as Pythagoras, who believed that ultimately the world consisted of numbers. Such a belief may appear odd, or even plain daft, to us. However, modern science's reason for believing that every-thing can ultimately be explained in terms of number is in fact much less convincing. It is simply an article of faith we have. It has no reason, proof or concrete support – other than the fact that we choose to see the world this way.

Pythagoras may have founded the mathematical view of the world, but the ancient Greek scientific view was formed by the philosopher Aristotle. Indeed, both of these great figures were regarded as philosophers in their time. Science was part of philosophy (which in ancient Greek means 'the study of wisdom'). Later, science came to be known as natural philosophy. Likewise the word mathematics, which was first used by Pythagoras, was derived from the ancient Greek word *mathema*, which meant 'something one learns', or science. It was only over the ensuing millennia that the words philosophy, mathematics and science gradually evolved their present separate meanings.

With all learning lumped together under the term philosophy, things soon became muddled. If different types of learning were to advance, they needed to be separated and categorized. This was Aristotle's great scientific achievement. He laid down the rules for the separate sciences.

Unfortunately Aristotle's greatest love was biology, and this was to have a catastrophic effect. The way Aristotle saw it, biology was fundamentally purposive. In order to understand the organs of plants or animals we had to seek to discover what they were for – in other words, their purpose. It may have helped to view biology like this, but it was to have disastrous effects on the other sciences. Aristotle insisted on seeing the world as organic, rather than mechanical. This meant that instead of following cause and effect, all objects fulfilled a purpose. Their behaviour inclined them towards the end which they were destined to serve.

No immediate purpose was apparent in astronomy, so Aristotle imposed one upon it. The heavenly bodies were by nature divine, so their purpose was to behave in a divine manner. This meant they had to move in a perfect, eternal and unchanging fashion – in other words, continue to orbit the heavens in perfect circles for eternity. The Earth on the other hand was not divine, so it didn't behave in this fashion. Instead it remained still, at the centre of the universe, with the heavenly bodies circling around it.

This view of the universe was to prevail for over two thousand years. Aristotle's effect on science was immensely beneficial in many fields, but eventually it became a stranglehold limiting further progress. In some fields, such as astronomy, it was detrimental from the word go. Heraclides, a contemporary of Aristotle, had already worked out that Venus and Mercury revolved around the Sun, and that the Earth moved through space. And within a few years of Aristotle's death, Aristarchus of Samos realized that the Earth orbited the Sun and rotated on its own axis. Unfortunately these discoveries were ignored because they didn't accord with Aristotle's teleological (purposive) world-view. Even Archimedes, who was a contemporary of Aristarchus and no mean astronomer himself, clung to Aristotle's view of the solar system. It is no accident that the main advances made by Archimedes were in the spheres least affected by Aristotle's organic teleology – namely physics and mathematics.

THE LIFE & WORKS OF ARCHIMEDES

Archimedes was born in 287 BC at Syracuse, the most powerful Greek city-state in Sicily. Syracuse had long aspired to a tradition of learning and sophistication, though with little success. In the previous century Plato had spent two spells here vainly attempting to instill some culture into the boorish local tyrant and his ignoramus son. Syracuse was strategically placed between the expanding Carthaginian Empire in north Africa and the embryo Roman Empire – it required something a little more resilient than philosophy or art to survive.

Despite this, there were men of culture in the city – and Archimedes' father Pheidias was one of them. Pheidias was an aristocrat and an astronomer of some renown. He was almost certainly a fine mathematician too. According to his son, he produced calculations estimating the ratio between the diameters of the Sun and the Moon.

Apart from odd snippets of information in his scientific and mathematical treatises, we know most about Archimedes from the Roman writer Plutarch who lived three centuries later. Plutarch had a great regard for many aspects of ancient Greek culture, and his best-known work *Parallel Lives* compares eminent Greeks with their Roman counterparts. However, the Romans simply weren't attuned to largely theoretical pursuits such as mathematics and physics, and Plutarch evidently didn't think much of Archimedes. The greatest scientist of the classical era appears as a mere passing insertion in the biography of the Roman general who inadvertently had him killed.

Archimedes may have been related to King Hieron II, the ruler of Syracuse, and was known to have remained close to him throughout his life. He may even have acted as tutor to Hieron's son.

As a young man Archimedes went to Alexandria to complete his education. By the early second century BC, Alexandria was becoming the greatest centre of learning in the

Mediterranean world, surpassing even Athens. The city had only been founded in 313 BC by Alexander the Great in the course of his campaign to conquer the world. And it was here that history's greatest megalomaniac was buried in a resplendent gold coffin in 323 BC. (The exact site of Alexander's tomb has been lost to history – though it was known to Ptolemy X, who surreptitiously replaced the gold coffin with an alabaster replica when he was strapped for cash.)

The famous Library at Alexandria was founded around the period of Archimedes' birth. By the time he arrived in Alexandria it almost certainly had at least a hundred thousand scrolls, including Aristotle's extensive collection (the greatest private library of the Greek era). The Library attracted scholars from all over the Hellenistic world, quickly establishing it as the pre-eminent centre of learning. It was run by some of the finest scholars of the time. The great geometer Euclid had probably died before Archimedes arrived in Alexandria, but he would certainly have read Euclid's works and studied with one of his pupils.

Euclid's definitive textbook *Elements* laid the

foundations of geometry. It starts with a set of simple self-evident definitions – 'a point has a position but no magnitude', 'a line is a length without breadth', 'a straight line passes evenly between its extreme points' and so forth. Using these definitions, Euclid then sets about proving a succession of theorems. Each ensuing theorem is based upon a predecessor, thus establishing an utterly rigorous procedure. (Inevitably, later geometers discovered the odd lacunae in this systematic masterpiece. But it was not until the Russian Lobachevsky developed a geometry of curved surfaces in the 19th century that the universality of Euclidian geometry was first seriously questioned.) Other books in *Elements* dealt with solid geometry and the theory of numbers, both of which were fields in which Archimedes was to excel.

Whilst studying at Alexandria, Archimedes got to know two mathematicians, with whom he was to remain in correspondence throughout his life. Archimedes was to spend most of his life working on his own in Syracuse, so it's worth knowing what little information there is about these two kindred spirits whom Archimedes regarded as colleagues. They were both fine mathematicians in their own right, though hardly the equal of Archimedes.

Conon of Samos was a friend who would almost certainly have known Aristarchus, a contemporary who came from the same island. It is likely that he knew Aristarchus's heliocentric theory before he moved to Alexandria, in which case he would certainly have discussed this with Archimedes. Conon too was an astronomer of note, and had dealings with the royal court in Alexandria. He is credited with discovering a new constellation of seven dim stars, which he sycophantically named *The Lock of Berenice* after a missing snippet of the queen's hair.

Eratosthenes, Archimedes' other great student pal, was a much more interesting character. He was an all-rounder who studied everything from geography to comedy. He also drew up the first chronological table of Greek history not to include any myths. Eratosthenes pronounced that Greek history had begun with the fall of Troy, which he boldly calculated had taken place in precisely 1184 BC (according to our system of dating). This was remarkably accurate: fainthearted modern scholars state that this event *probably* took place in *about* 1250 BC.

Eratosthenes invented the word 'philologist' (meaning 'lover of learning', or scholar), which he used to describe himself. He drew the first map of the (Mediterranean) world which included latitude and longitude. He also drew the first meridian through Alexandria, south to Syene (now Aswan). Unfortunately, this meridian was out of true by over 25° – a fact which any sailor could have pointed out to him. (But the first scholars did not believe in consulting with experts in the field, a tradition which has proved one of the more lasting legacies of ancient Greek scholarship.)

The inaccuracy of Eratosthenes' meridian was to affect his greatest discovery – but it does not detract from its brilliance. Eratosthenes was the first to make an accurate calculation of the earth's circumference. How he did this remains a lasting testament to his genius.

Eratosthenes knew that on a certain day at noon the sun shone to the bottom of a deep well in Cyrene, indicating that it was directly over-head. On the same day at noon in Alexandria he measured that a perpendicular stick cast a shadow corresponding to ⅟₅₀th of a circle. He then made calculations based on the assumption that the sun was so far away its rays were virtually parallel at both spots (an astonishingly far-sighted assumption for this era). Using the known distance between Syene and Alexandria, Eratosthenes was able to work out that the earth's circumference was 50 times this distance.

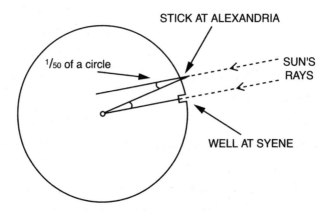

Considering the nature of his equipment (a stick and a well), and his technical information (the faulty meridian and imprecise contemporary notions of distance), his result was astonishingly accurate – to within 4% of present calculations.

Eratosthenes became head of the Library at

Alexandria, and may well have lived to the ripe old age of 80 (another remarkable figure for his era). At the end he became blind, and was unable to read. This provoked him to the ultimate bibliophile's response, and he committed suicide.

When Archimedes left Alexandria, legend has it that he travelled to Spain. If so, he must already have become an accomplished engineer and inventor. According to a story mentioned by Leonardo da Vinci in his notebooks, Archimedes acted as a military engineer for King Ecliderides of Cilodastri in a maritime war against the English. Archimedes is said to have invented a machine which fired burning pitch onto the enemy ships. Another more credible report by the Sicilian historian Diodorus, who lived in the first century BC, speaks of Archimedes' Screw being used for pumping water from the silver mines of Rio Tinto in southern Spain. Diodorus claims that Archimedes invented his screw for just this purpose.

Other reports speak of Archimedes returning to Egypt for a second trip, where he was employed on the large-scale irrigation works to control the flooding of the Nile Delta. Such works are known to have been constructed during this period.

Whether or not there is any truth in these stories, Archimedes certainly invented an ingenious screw which was used as a water pump. (The Archimedes Screw remains in use in the Nile Delta to this day, and the same principle is used for raising grain and sand when loading bulk carriers.)

In its simplest form the screw consists of a central pole with a thread wrapped around it in a spiral:

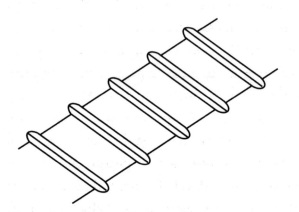

When this is inserted into a cylinder, and turned, water is carried up the screw and disgorged, as in the slightly more sophisticated device overleaf:

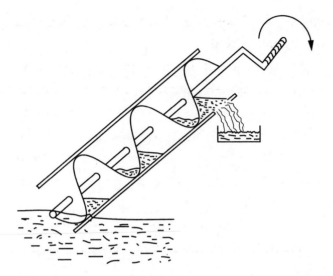

Archimedes' early fame was due to his practical engineering abilities and inventions. Yet amongst all his written works – of which ten treatises have come down to us – no mention is made of these practical devices. According to Plutarch: 'he did not deign to leave behind him any written work on such subjects; he regarded as sordid and ignoble the construction of instruments, and in general every art directed to use and profit, and he only strove after those things which, in their beauty and excellence, remain beyond all contact with the common needs of life.'

This intellectual snobbery derived from Plato,

whose philosophy decreed that the only real world was that of timeless abstractions (or eternal ideas, as he called them). The particular world around us was mere illusion. This is an impossible attitude for any scientist to adopt, and Archimedes largely ignored its unreality. Despite this, however, elements of it infected his work: this was the prevailing ethos amongst the learned men of the period. Archimedes undoubtedly considered his theoretical work to be his *real* work, with the practical side as mere bread and butter. Though whether he went so far as to regard practical science as 'sordid and ignoble' is another matter. As we shall see, Archimedes was well aware of 'the common needs of life' in the warring world of the third century BC Mediterranean. (The snooty attitude foisted on Archimedes by the likes of Plato and Plutarch is another resilient tradition which has continued to hamper human progress since ancient Greek times.)

Back in Syracuse, Archimedes devoted himself to pure mathematics, putting in the long and arduous hours of theoretical work which were to establish him as the finest mathematical mind for almost two thousand years to come. Any individual who spends most of his waking life in obsessive mental activity attracts the usual corny anecdotes, and Archimedes was no exception. According to Plutarch: 'He was so bewitched by thought that he always forgot to eat and ignored his appearance. When things became too bad his friends would forcibly insist that he had a bath, and make sure that afterwards he anointed himself with sweet-smelling oils. Yet even then he would remain lost to the world, drawing geometric figures. . .'

This is just the kind of clichéd figure one would expect. But it's worth remembering that in the second century BC scientists were as rare as the solar eclipses they predicted. Such characteristics, accompanied by otherwise rational behaviour, were a new phenomenon. The stereotypical scientist had had little time to develop, which means that these objections concerning Archimedes' personal hygiene and sartorial appearance may well contain an element of truth. It looks as if Archimedes played a leading role in creating this stereotype – setting a trend for scientists which shows every sign of lasting well into the third millenium AD.

Archimedes would probably have been quite

happy to continue in this malodorous meta-physical fashion, but King Hieron evidently reckoned that such behaviour set a bad example to his Syracusan subjects. According to Plutarch, Hieron 'emphatically requested and persuaded [Archimedes] to occupy himself in some tangible manner with the demands of reality'. More specifically, he ordered Archimedes down to the docks, to see if he could sort out the mess his royal shipbuilders had got themselves into. They had just finished constructing a large luxuriously appointed ship called the *Syracusia*, which Hieron wished to present to King Ptolemy of Egypt. According to contemporary reports the ship must have weighed well over 4,000 tons (equal to a modern 300-crew destroyer). Indeed, it was so heavy that the shipbuilders found themselves unable to launch it.

Enter superman Archimedes. How precisely he managed to launch this beached behemoth remains unclear – but presumably it involved a system of pulleys, for Archimedes is reported to have launched *Syracusia* single-handedly. It was on this occasion that he made his celebrated boast: 'Give me a place to stand, and I can move the earth.'

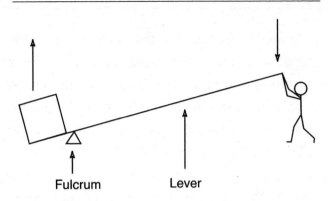

Fulcrum   Lever

Archimedes' famous remark reveals his understanding of the fulcrum. This is literally a support,
or prop, placed so as to enable a comparatively
small amount of pressure to lift a comparatively
large weight. The fulcrum can be used either to
support a lever or, as in the case of the *Syracusia*, a
system of pulley wheels. One of Archimedes'
finest works, *On the Equilibrium of Planes*, is
devoted to levers, showing how to determine the
centre of gravity of various plane (ie, two-dimen-
sional) figures. As in all his works, Archimedes
stuck to the format established by Euclid.
Postulates (or definitions) are followed by propositions (or theorems) which are then proved, each
proof following from a previous proof.

At the outset Archimedes established the
central principle of levers. This decrees that 'two

magnitudes balance at distances reciprocally proportional to their magnitudes.'

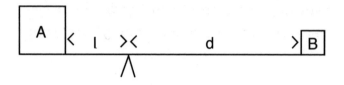

For the two weights A and B to balance in the above figure:

A is to B as d is to l

$$A:B = d:l \quad \text{or} \quad \frac{A}{B} = \frac{d}{l}$$

Archimedes introduced the notion which we now know as 'centre of gravity', and showed how to calculate it.

This may well have been known to previous mathematicians, but Archimedes probably formalized the theoretical basis for its calculation, and certainly extended its application. Later in this work Archimedes established how to discover the centre of gravity for parallelograms, triangles and parabolic segments. Most, if not all of this, is original work. *On the Equilibrium of Planes* laid the foundations of theoretical physics.

However, Archimedes considered that his

most important contributions were in solid geometry. His treatise *On the Sphere and the Cylinder* proved that the surface of a sphere is four times the surface area of the circle which circumvents it (e.g. a slice taken through the globe at the equator). In other words:

$S = 4 \pi r^2$

Archimedes also proved that the volume of a sphere is ⅔ of the cylinder into which it fits.

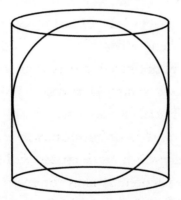

As a result he was able to show that the formula for the volume of a sphere is:

$V = \tfrac{4}{3} \pi r^3$

Archimedes considered that his discovery of the relation between a sphere and its containing cylinder was his finest achievement – so much so that he asked for the diagram of a sphere inscribed in a cylinder to be carved on his tomb.

Archimedes also made another theoretical discovery about a sphere thus inscribed in a cylinder – namely that the surface area of the sphere is equal to the curved surface of the enclosing cylinder.

His practical work with spherical objects was equally impressive. He is said to have constructed two spherical planetaria which were so admired that they were carried back to Rome as booty after the fall of Syracuse. The first of these was almost certainly a hemisphere whose inner surface contained a map of the heavens. This may have been beautiful in its own right, but the second was undoubtedly a masterpiece of mechanical ingenuity. This consisted of an open planetarium with moving parts which precisely mirrored the plan of the universe as conceived by Eudoxus of Cnidus, a friend of Plato, who had lived the mathematical life in Athens during the previous century.

According to Eudoxus, the universe consisted of a number of transparent concentric spheres, each of which supported a planet. As the spheres moved, so did the planets revolve along their paths. (Adapting an old Pythagorean idea,

Eudoxus claimed that the movement of these spheres against one another produced a heavenly 'music of the spheres', which was so beautiful that it could not be heard by human ears.) Eudoxus's conception of the universe, with the earth at its centre and the planets revolving around it, was to have a profound influence on Aristotle. And once the great Aristotle had laid down the law that the earth was the centre of the universe, even Archimedes felt bound to accept this view. His intricate planetarium is said to have traced the motions of the sun, moon and planets about the earth, relative to the sphere of fixed stars, during the course of one day. It could also be set to illustrate the successive phases of the moon and lunar eclipses. Scholars are of the opinion that it must have been driven by some kind of mechanism similar to a water-clock.

In Rome, Archimedes' planetarium with moving parts attracted widespread wonder for centuries to come. Ovid and Cicero both refer to it. In the fourth century AD the Latin scholar Lactantius, tutor to Constantine the Great's son, even used Archimedes' wonder for one of the first Christian proofs of God's existence. According to

Lactantius, if the intelligence of a human being was capable of producing such a wondrous thing, there must be an even greater intelligence which was capable of producing the object which the human intelligence sought to imitate. (By this period, circularity was not just limited to the orbits of the heavenly bodies about the earth.)

Archimedes' planetarium was almost certainly lost during the sack of Rome by the Visigoths in 410 AD, but the faulty idea upon which it was based was to last another thousand years. Aristotle's notion of an earth–centred solar system was maintained as an article of faith by the Catholic Church throughout the Middle Ages.

When it came to the planetarium even Archimedes seems to have been impressed by his technical wizardry. Breaking the habit of a lifetime he wrote a treatise *On Sphere-making*. There are several tantalizing references to this in classical sources, but we will never know for certain the true nature of Archimedes' masterpiece, as this treatise is now lost.

A masterpiece which *has* survived is Archimedes' short work *Measurement of the Circle*, which contains one of his finest pieces of geometric argument. This gives the ratio of the circumference of a circle to its diameter, which enabled him to produce a remarkably accurate approximation of π. The method he used here pointed the way to one of the major discoveries of mathematics.

Archimedes calculated the area of a circle by discovering the limits between which this area lay, and then gradually narrowing these limits until they approximated the actual area. This he did by inscribing within the circle a regular polygon, and then circumscribing the circle with a similar polygon.

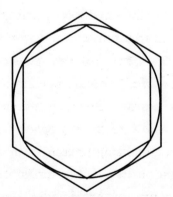

Archimedes began with two hexagons, and by doubling the sides and repeating the process eventually reached polygons of 96 sides. He calculated the area of the inner polygon, which gave the lower limit of the area of the circle. He then calculated the area of the outer polygon, which gave the upper limit. By this method he was able to calculate that:

$$3 \tfrac{10}{71} < \pi < 3 \tfrac{1}{7}$$

In decimal, this gives the equation:

$$3.14084 < \pi < 3.142858$$

The accuracy of this can be seen by the fact that to seven figures we now know:

$$\pi = 3.1415927$$

Archimedes' major innovation here was to use *approximation* instead of *precise equality*. Euclid had indicated this as a method, but didn't seriously apply it or see its possibilities. Archimedes saw that it was often sufficient to make two comparatively easy approximations of an answer, which gave an upper and a lower limit – between which the answer lay. The more exactitude required, the narrower the limits. For example, in the previous diagram the sides of the polygon could be increased towards an upper limit of infinite, thus narrowing the difference between the upper and lower limits to an infinitessimally small amount. This is the beginnings of calculus, though it was to be nearly 2,000 years before anyone advanced on this idea. Not until 1666 did Newton formulate the essentials of differential and integral calculus.

However, some are of the opinion that Archimedes did in fact use integral calculus in his treatise *On Conoids and Spheroids*. This treatise expands geometry beyond the rigid parameters imposed upon it by Plato and his mystical attitude towards forms, mathematical or otherwise. (Plato believed that these forms – or ideas – were the ultimate reality, out of which the world was made: a recognizable development from Pythagoras' belief that 'all is number'.) Plato believed in God and geometry. According to his famous saying: 'God ever geometrizes.' This was how God had formed the world. Therefore true geometry was limited to ideal forms, pure timeless figures such as could be constructed using only a compass and ruler. (Though why God's geometry set should be limited to a compass and a ruler remains unclear.) Figures which could not be constructed using only a compass and ruler were dismissively referred to as 'mechanical', implying that they could only be formed by mechanical motion, and thus were neither timeless nor perfect. They belonged only in the realm of practical mathematical application.

Archimedes chose to ignore this arbitrary distinction, but he was virtually alone in doing so. Geometry was to remain crippled by Plato's mystical superstition for two millenia until the French philosopher and mathematician Descartes broke the mould in the 17th century. Indeed, remnants of this distinction persist to this day in our notions of 'pure' and 'applied' mathematics.

In *On Conoids and Spheroids* Archimedes dealt with the four conic sections – circle, ellipse, parabola and hyperbola.

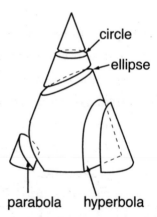

Of the conic sections, only the circle is a classic geometric figure in the Platonic sense.

When these segments are revolved about their axis they form solids. For instance, a two dimensional circle revolved about its axis (its diameter) will form a three dimensional sphere. An ellipse will form a flattened sphere shape known as an ellipsoid, and so forth.

Archimedes showed how to calculate the volumes of such three-dimensional shapes.

Essentially this meant calculating the area beneath the curve involved, and then revolving this about its axis to find the volume. (Like finding the area of a semi-circle, from which we move on to calculate the volume of the sphere formed by revolving the semi-circle 360°.) The method used by Archimedes for calculating the area beneath a curve involved much the same idea as his calculation of the area of a circle using inscribed and circumscribed polygons. We can use this to calculate the area beneath a semi-circular curve, in the following manner.

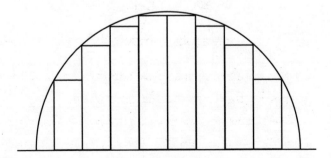

If we divide the semi-circle into parallel strips of equal width, and cut off the tips so that each strip becomes rectangular, we can easily calculate the area occupied by all the sections. The narrower the strips become, the less will be the area of the discarded tips. As the number of strips approaches infinite, so the discarded area becomes infinitessimally small, and the total area of the strips approaches the area of the semi-circle, which is its upper limit. This, in simplified form, is integral calculus.

In another treatise, called *On Spirals*, Archimedes used a method very similar to differential calculus.

This treatise dealt with another non-Platonic geometric shape, namely the so-called spiral of Archimedes.

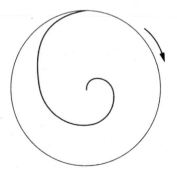

Which continues to become:

This spiral Archimedes defined in exact but exacting fashion as follows:

'If a straight line drawn in a plane revolve at a uniform rate about one extremity which remains fixed and return from the position from which it started, and if, at the same time as the line revolves, a point move at a uniform rate along the straight line beginning from the extremity which remains fixed, the point will describe a spiral in the plane.' Basically, this is the path followed by an ant travelling directly from the centre to the rim of a spinning disc, as seen by the bemused overhead observer patiently waiting to put on a new disc.

Archimedes solved the problem of how to discover the tangent to any point on the spiral.

Differential calculus solves the problem of how to find the tangent to any point on any curve. From this it can be seen that Archimedes was within a whisker of discovering differential calculus. However, his calculations involving his spiral did succeed in solving two of the three classic geometric problems which had long pre-occupied mathematicians throughout the ancient world. These were:

1. How to trisect an angle.
2. How to draw a cube which has double the volume of a given cube.
3. How to construct a square equal to a circle.

Archimedes showed how to trisect an angle by an ingenious use of his spiral.

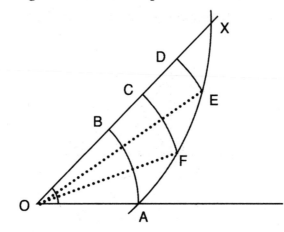

In order to trisect the angle XOA, draw across it a segment of an Archimedes spiral XEFA. (Evenly open a compass along a rotating ruler.) Draw an arc from A to B with centre O. Trisect BX into BC, CD and DX. Draw arcs with centre O from C to F, and from D to E. OE and OF trisect the angle XOA. (From this, it can be seen that the Archimedes spiral may be used to divide an angle into any number of equal parts.)

Archimedes also worked out how to solve the third of the celebrated problems of antiquity – namely, how to construct a square equal to a circle ie, one whose sides add up to the same length as the circumference of the circle. This is the famous problem, known as 'squaring the circle'.

To do this Archimedes also used his spiral.

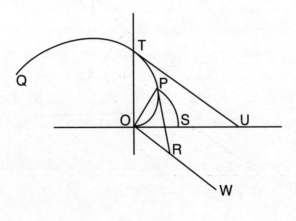

Put simply, Archimedes proceeded as follows:
P is any point on the spiral. The line OW forms a right-angle with OP. The tangent at P intersects OW at R. The arc PS has radius OP and intersects with initial direction of fly setting out from O.

Archimedes demonstrated that OR is the same length as the arc PS.

From this it follows that OU was the same length as a quarter of the circumference of a circle radius OT.

Draw this circle, and it is squared by a square drawn on base OU.

Although Archimedes solved this problem, the question of how to 'square the circle' continued to defeat all comers until well beyond the Middle Ages. Indeed, it remains unsolved to this day. But how come – if Archimedes found the answer?

According to Plato's rules, in other words according to classical geometry, Archimedes was cheating – because his spiral is a 'mechanical figure'. It cannot be drawn using only a compass and ruler.

No one has yet managed to solve any of the three celebrated 'problems of antiquity' using

classical geometry (ie, only a compass and ruler).
And they never will. In 1882 it was eventually
proved that none of these problems could be
solved using only a compass and ruler.

Relevant to the previous treatises is a further
work by Archimedes called *Quadrature of the
Parabola*. As with all his treatises, Archimedes
opened with a letter. These letters were usually
addressed to one of his Alexandrian friends. From
what he says it is clear that he was aware of the
importance of his work, and had no wish to keep
it to himself. He was keen for his work to take its
place in the growing body of scientific knowledge which was accumulating at the Library in
Alexandria, so that it could circulate amongst
those who studied there. Living a thousand miles
across the sea in Sicily, Archimedes seems to have
remained somewhat isolated from this centre of
learning. Or so his opening letter in *Quadrature of
the Parabola* implies. It begins:

'Archimedes to Dositheus, greetings.

I grieved when I heard that Conon, who
was my friend during his lifetime, was dead.
He was not only a friend but also an admirable

mathematician. I have learned that you were acquainted with him, and are also versed in geometry. For this reason I am writing to you the news I had intended sending to Conon. This concerns a certain geometrical theorem which has not been investigated before, but has now been investigated by me. I first discovered this theorem by means of mechanics and then demonstrated it by means of geometry.'

Here we again see the conflict between classical and mechanical geometry. Archimedes invariably felt the need to demonstrate his theorems by the rigorous classical method. Though indicatively, it was the mechanical method that enabled him to discover it in the first place.

He goes on to describe the problem: 'to square the segment bounded by a straight line and a section of a right-angled cone [in other words, a parabola].' He then announces his discovery 'that every segment bounded by a straight line and a section of a right-angled cone [a parabola] is four-thirds of the triangle which has the same base and equal height with the segment.'

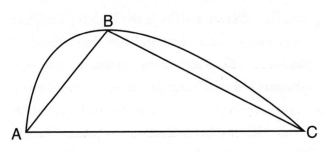

In other words: triangle ABC × ⅓ = parabolic segment ABC.

The mechanical method Archimedes used to discover this involved finding the area beneath the curve – again, a problem involving the method of integral calculus.

Yet the 'demands of reality' would keep interrupting Archimedes in his geometric dream world. Once more, the King required his services. This famous but unlikely story has several sources, indicating that it may well have a basis in some similar truth. The most reliable source is probably the Roman architect Vitruvius, even though he was writing two centuries after the events he described. According to Vitruvius, King Hieron chose to dedicate a gold wreath to the gods to celebrate his continuing good fortune. He commissioned a local Syracusan artist, but when the artist returned with the completed wreath Hieron became suspicious. He felt certain that the artist had adulterated the gold with less expensive silver, and then pocketed the profit. Hieron had the wreath weighed, but it came to the same weight as the gold the artist had been given. Hieron called in Archimedes, but even he was initially stumped. He promised to go away and think about it.

One morning, several days later, Archimedes was still pondering this problem when he stepped into a bath (a rare occurrence this, judging from other contemporary accounts). As he immersed himself further in the bath he noticed that more and more water flowed over the edge. In a flash he understood how to solve the problem of Hieron's wreath.

According to the legend, Archimedes became so excited at this discovery that he leapt from the bath and at once set off home to write it down. As he ran naked through the streets he was heard to shout: 'Eureka! Eureka!' (I have found it!)

Whether or not this story is true, it will remain forever attached to Archimedes. (As everyone knows, history is not what actually happened, but what we like to think happened.) To this day, scientists – and lesser mortals – frequently refer to the 'Eureka Moment' when they suddenly understand the solution to a problem. But what exactly had Archimedes understood?

According to Vitruvius, Archimedes asked Hieron for a lump of gold weighing the same as the wreath. This he then immersed in a pot filled to the brim with water, and measured the overflow. After this he immersed the wreath in a tub of water, and measured the overflow. This came to more than the gold, thus proving that the gold in the wreath had been adulterated. Archimedes had understood that solids of differing density displace differing amounts of water – because when they are the same weight they must occupy differing amounts of space.

The story of Archimedes leaping from the bath is traditionally linked with his discovery of the principle of hydrostatics. This appears in Archimedes' treatise *On Floating Bodies*, which is generally reckoned to be the founding work on hydrostatics. Simply put, Archimedes' principle states that a floating body will displace its own weight in fluid. This may seems obvious to us, but it was not so to the ancients. Until Archimedes produced his principle, no one knew precisely what floating meant. They had no way of *knowing* whether something would float or not. Yet surely shipbuilders knew that ships floated, without needing a mathematician to tell them so? Of course they did.

But ships were now becoming larger and much more sophisticated. As we've already seen, King Hieron's *Syracusia* was similar in tonnage to a modern destroyer, as was the ancient Greek fighting ship the trireme – so named because it had no less than three banks of oars (each heaved by a row of sweating galley slaves). By Archimedes' time there were such things as quinqueremes, which had *five* banks of oars. Scholars consider it most unlikely that in this case the banks of oars were stacked on top of each other. Yet it's a fair bet that they were in the first launched example – which inevitably toppled over (along with the head of the naval architect responsible.) Before Archimedes discovered the principle of hydrostatics, a shipbuilder had no way of *knowing* if his ship would float, or displace enough water in such a way as to remain floating upright.

But this was not all that Archimedes established in the new field of hydrostatics, which he was single-handedly creating in his treatise *On Floating Bodies*. Perhaps more interestingly to modern readers, he claimed: 'The surface of any fluid at rest is the surface of a sphere whose centre is the same as that of the earth.' In other words, neither the surface of the sea, nor the surface of water in a bathtub, is flat. It curves, aligning itself as a segment of a circle around the centre of the earth. And this he backed up with a mathematical proof.

The ancients were well aware that the earth was a globe – superstitions about sailing so far that one eventually fell off the edge of the world were seen as old sailors' tales. The persistence of such superstitions through the Middle Ages was simply due to woolly thinking and the introduction of religious and quasi-Aristotelian concepts into the scientific field. As we can see, both Archimedes and his friend Eratosthenes were already assuming the earth was a globe in mathematical proofs in the third century BC.

The laws of hydrostatics, as established by Archimedes, were to remain unchallenged (or ignored) for 1,800 years – until they were improved upon by the French mathematician and religious thinker Blaise Pascal. No other scientific field has been started, and then simply stopped in its tracks for almost two millennia.

In the second book of *On Floating Bodies*, Archimedes created one of the finest works of pure mathematical reasoning produced in any age. This deals with paraboloids of revolution (formed when a parabola is revolved about its axis). Archimedes demonstrated the positions in which these paraboloids would float in liquids of different densities. An example of the subtlety of his propositions gives but a hint of the subtlety of his mathematical procedure: 'Given a right segment of a paraboloid of revolution lighter than a fluid . . . if the segment be placed in the fluid so that its base is entirely submerged, it will never rest in such a position that the base touches the surface of the fluid at one point only.' In other words, it would never float as in the following diagram (and he managed to prove this).

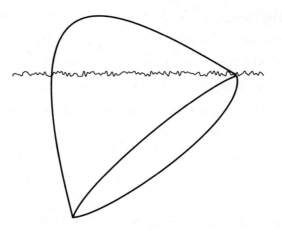

On Floating Bodies was the work of one of the greatest mathematicians of all time at the height of his powers, addressed to the brotherhood of mathematicians of all time. Prodigies cut their teeth on such works, others end up at the dentist. More amenable to the layman is Archimedes' most popular treatise *The Sand Reckoner*. This was addressed to King Gelon of Syracuse, who succeeded his father King Hieron II in 216 BC. It's more than likely that Archimedes acted at some stage as Gelon's tutor. He seems to have been well aware of Gelon's intellectual capacity – which appears to have been unusually adequate, for the son of a tyrant. *The Sand Reckoner* may be aimed at the layman, but it in no sense 'talks down' to the reader. On the contrary, it is one of the most imaginative and inspiring short works ever written about number (admittedly, not a field overburdened with such works).

The Sand Reckoner succeeds in being both poetic and rigidly mathematical right from its opening letter, which is worth quoting at some length:

'There are some, King Gelon, who think that the number of grains of the sand is infinite in multitude; and I mean by the sand not only that which exists about Syracuse and the rest of Sicily but also that which is found in every region whether inhabited or uninhabited. Again there are some who, without regarding it as infinite, yet think that no number has been named which is great enough to exceed its multitude. And it is clear that they who hold this view, if they imagined a mass made up of sand in other respects as large as the mass of the earth, including in it all the seas and hollows of the earth filled up to a height equal to that of the highest mountains, would be many times further still from recognizing that any number could be expressed which exceeded the multitude of the sand so taken. But I will try to show you by means of geometrical proofs, which you will be able to follow, that, of the numbers named by me and given in the work which I sent to Zeuxippus, some exceed not only the number of the mass of sand equal in magnitude to the earth filled up in the way described, but also that of a mass equal in magnitude to the universe.'

In *The Sand Reckoner* Archimedes set about overcoming the limitations of the Greek numerical system. As far as we can tell, this was essentially a decimal system borrowed from the Egyptians. It had no concept of zero, and an upper limit. The highest number was a myriad, which was the equivalent in modern notation to 10,000. (The ancient Greeks would not of course have expressed it in this fashion, with zeros.) Archimedes argued quite logically that if there were traditional names for numbers up to a myriad, it was therefore possible to express numbers up to a myriad myriads (100,000,000). These numbers he called the numbers of the *first order*. He then continued:

'Suppose the number 100,000,000 to be the [first] unit of the *second order*, and let the *second order* consist of the numbers from that unit up to $(100,000,000)^2$.

Let this again be the [first] unit of the *third order* of numbers ending with $(100,000,000)^3$; and so on until we reach the *100,000,000th order* of numbers ending with $(100,000,000)^{100,000,000}$, which we will call P.'

Archimedes then continued in a similar fashion, until he came to the number $P^{100,000,000}$. This is so large that if it was written out fully there would not be enough room in the universe to contain it.

Archimedes was making a revolutionary point here. He was demonstrating that mathematics was larger than the universe. As promised in his introductory letter, Archimedes went on to show that mathematics could even number the grains of sand needed to fill the universe, and still have numbers left over to spare.

Archimedes was probably the first to elaborate in detail the mathematics of large numbers. He set out calculations which showed that 'the number of grains of sand which could be contained in a sphere of the size of our "universe" [ie, what we would call the solar system] is less than 1,000 units of the *seventh order* of numbers.' In other words: 10^{51}.

And how do *we* arrive at this last figure? According to Archimedes, the *second order* of numbers is 100,000,000 to $(100,000,000)^2$.

So the *seventh order* of numbers must be $(100,000,000)^6$ to $(100,000,000)^7$.

But the start of the *seventh order*: $(100,000,000)^6 = 10^{48.}$

So 1,000 (10^3) units of $10^{48} = 10^3 \times 10^{48} = 10^{3+48} = 10^{51}$ (demonstrating that it is possible for most of us to deal in macro-mathematical numbers if we put our mind to it.)

In order to undertake these calculations, Archimedes made various assumptions. These included: 'The perimeter of the earth is about 3,000,000 stadia and not greater.' (One stadium was approximately ⅛th of a mile: modern calculations set the equator at around 200,000 stadia.) 'The diameter of the earth is greater than the diameter of the moon, and the diameter of the sun is greater than the diameter of the earth.' (Most ancient astronomers had by now come to this conclusion.) 'The diameter of the sun is about 30 times the diameter of the moon and not greater.' (Previous estimates had put it at no more than 20 times larger. It is in fact around 400 times larger.) What is most remarkable is not so much the comparative accuracy of such figures, but that Archimedes was using them at all in calculations. This was the era when the most advanced form of land transport was the chariot, the only observational instrument was the human eye, and the extremities of the known world petered out at the fringes of north-western Europe and the borders of India. This gives an indication of just how far Greek theoretical knowledge had outstripped practical application. Such a discrepancy has never again occurred in the entire history of human knowledge, with the exception of our present century.

In *The Sand Reckoner* Archimedes also outlined the heliocentric scheme of the universe which had been proposed some years earlier by Aristarchus of Samos. Archimedes rightly concluded that Aristarchus's ideas meant 'the universe is many times greater than now so-called'. Unfortunately he dismissed such conclusions. It is perhaps indicative that Archimedes' uncharacteristically fuzzy thinking at this point contains the two flaws which were to mar much Greek scientific thinking. He argues abstractly, with no reference to observation, and he also appears to assume Aristotelian notions of a harmonious and purposeful universe.

It is difficult to see how Archimedes squared this latter view with his revolutionary understanding that the entire universe could be contained and described by mathematics. Archimedes' understanding of this idea was very much like our own – far in advance of the mystical Pythagorian 'all is number'. By the third century BC mathematics had developed, in part through Archimedes' own contribution, into an instrument of subtlety and sophistication well beyond Aristotelian notions of harmony and purpose. Yet in certain vital fields the old mind-set prevailed. Even Archimedes had not succeeded entirely in shedding the ancient blinkers. (Such a curious hangover is not unique amongst great minds. Newton continued throughout his life to believe in alchemy, and as late as the 19th century the German philosopher Hegel held that there could only be seven planets for the same mystical reason as Pythagoras.)

All of the previously mentioned works of Archimedes (except *On Sphere-making*) survived in one form or another into the Middle Ages, and from thence to the present day. Many others are known to have disappeared, including his *Method Concerning Mechanical Theorems*. Medieval and ancient references to this treatise indicated that it was undoubtedly one of Archimedes' major works, possibly even *the* major work.

In 1899, a Greek scholar working in the library of the monastery of the Holy Sepulchre in Jerusalem made passing reference to a medieval palimpsest. (This is a parchment scroll where the original writing has been erased to make way for a second text.) The palimpsest contained a 13th century euchologion of Greek Orthodox rituals and prayers. But beneath this a shadowy previous text containing mathematical symbols was still just discernable. Reference to this manuscript came to the attention of the Danish classical philologist J.L. Heiberg, one of the greatest historians of mathematics. Heiberg finally managed to track the palimpsest down to Constantinople

(Istanbul) in 1906, whereupon he made a number of sensational discoveries. The original script on the palimpsest contained texts of Archimedes' work dating from the tenth century. And amongst these was his long lost masterpiece *Method Concerning Mechanical Theorems*. Other texts confirmed that *The Stomachion* – for so long discounted as a work by Archimedes, even by Heiberg himself – was indeed one of his works.

The contents of the *Method* proved to be no less sensational than its discovery. Aptly, it was addressed to Archimedes' most brilliant colleague Eratosthenes in Alexandria, and it disclosed nothing less than the secrets of his genius. It is the work in which Archimedes shows *how* he made his discoveries – the way his mind proceeded towards mathematical truths, well before he was able to prove them.

Prior to the discovery of this treatise, mathematicians had been aware that this factor had been missing from Archimedes' works. His theorems were all backed by rigorous proofs, but it was evident that he couldn't have used these proofs to *discover* the truths they contained. Only when reading the *Method* does it become obvious that Archimedes relied heavily upon 'mechanical' method to reach many of his discoveries. He used this forerunner of calculus, involving increasingly small quantities, to 'exhaust' spaces which could not be accounted for. For example, by narrowing the oblong strips beneath a curve.

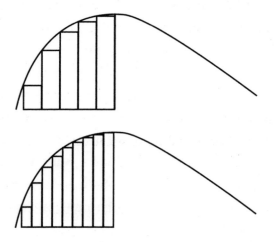

As previously mentioned, the great innovation of this method of 'exhaustion' was that it relied upon *approximation*. Prior to this, mathematicians had only thought in terms of precise answers. A calculation was either right or wrong. This concept of *approaching ever-closer* to the answer, or of narrowing the limits *between which the answer lay*, was entirely new. So much so that it wasn't accepted as proof, by the rigorous standards insisted upon by the Greeks. Even Archimedes himself only looked upon this 'mechanical' method as 'a heuristic device' ie, useful for arriving at truths.

Yet Archimedes was well aware of the importance of his discovery. As he explained to Eratosthenes: 'I consider it necessary to expound this method for two reasons. Firstly, I have already mentioned it to you without explaining what it is, and don't want you to think that I was merely bluffing. And secondly, because I am convinced that it will be of great value to mathematics. My contemporaries, and my successors, will be able to use it to discover further new theorems, such as have not yet occurred to me.' Archimedes was not mistaken. Indeed, this prophesy was eventually to be fulfilled beyond all possible expectation. Calculus, which developed out of his method, has been described as 'the most useful mathematical tool ever invented for describing the workings of the real world'.

Other 'lost' works by Archimedes have not yet been rediscovered – and almost certainly never will be. Many believe that the originals of these works went up in smoke when the Library at Alexandria burnt down in 47 BC. This unique cultural catastrophe was to cast a long shadow, playing no small role in the intellectual inertia of the Middle Ages. Had all the works of Archimedes been available at the beginning of the second millennium, it is nice to think that they might have tipped the balance – causing medieval thought to become a thing of rigour rather than ritual.

References to lost works by Archimedes appear in a variety of sources, from Ovid to Lucretius. But these seldom give more than a hint of their contents. Most intriguing is the treatise on catoptrics, dealing with reflection and mirrors. In this he is said to have investigated refraction (some one and a half millennia before anyone else thought to examine this phenomenon scientifically). According to the contemporary Alexandrian geometer Pappus, Archimedes also wrote a treatise on semi-regular polyhedrons. These are three-dimensional convex figures whose faces are made up of two or more types of regular polygon, and which are identical at their vertices. (A similar principle is used in the

contruction of a football.) A simple example of a
semi-regular polyhedron is a truncated cube.

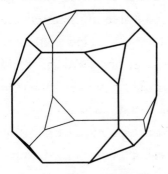

More complex is a truncated dodecahedron – a
regular twelve-sided solid with its corners lopped
off.

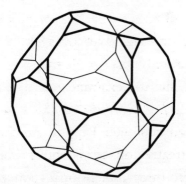

In all, Archimedes investigated 13 such figures,
which are now known as Archimedean poly-
hedra after him.

Several sources refer to a mathematical chest-nut which Archimedes is said to have sent to Eratosthenes, challenging the mathematicians of Alexandria to solve it. This is the celebrated 'Cattle Problem'. The problem has only come down to us in the form of a poem, which couldn't possibly have been written by Archimedes – who was all fingers and thumbs when it came to poetic feet. This has prompted doubt over whether Archimedes was the origina-tor of this problem, though its sheer complexity speaks in favour of this assumption.

The poem begins in deceptive Arcadian sim-plicity:

> 'Helios the sun god took his herd of cows and bulls
> To the isle of Sicily and grazed them on the hills . . .'

These cattle were of four different colours. Some were white, some grey, others brown and yet others dappled.

The amount of dappled bulls was less than the amount of white bulls by ⅚ of the amount of grey bulls.

This was less than the amount of grey bulls by $\frac{9}{20}$ of the amount of brown bulls.

This was less than the amount of brown bulls by $\frac{13}{42}$ of the amount of white bulls.

Meanwhile the amount of white cows was $\frac{7}{12}$ the amount of grey cows and grey bulls added together.

The amount of grey cows was $\frac{9}{20}$ the amount of brown cows and brown bulls added together.

The amount of brown cows was $\frac{11}{30}$ of the amount of dappled cows and dappled bulls added together.

The amount of dappled cows was $\frac{13}{42}$ of the amount of white cows and white bulls.

How many cows and how many bulls were there of each colour in the herd of Helios the sun god?

We can only surmise the reaction of the Alexandrian sages to this challenge to their mathematical manhood – or womanhood. (Though they remained rare, there are known to have been a few women mathematicians during this period. The most celebrated was perhaps Agnodice, who was forced to disguise herself in men's clothing to study at Alexandria; Axiothea, on the other hand, adopted this guise of her own volition when she lectured at Plato's Academy. Another Alexandrian scholar, Iphigenia of Cos, is said to have demonstrated that a proof by her tutor, the great geometer Pappus, was in fact fraudulent.)

But back to a different sort of bull. Archimedes' Cattle Problem can be expressed in formulae involving eight unknowns. It is a problem in indeterminate analysis, which means it has more than one correct set of answers. However, the evidence indicates that even Archimedes himself had difficulty here. He may have succeeded in baffling his rival Alexandrians, but he also succeeded in baffling himself. Even the lowest set of correct answers involves millions. For instance, the lowest correct amount of white bulls is 10,366,482, and white cows 7,206,360. Archimedes' lowest (and only) answers are around 80 times these figures, and even then are not quite right. (And this time he didn't have the excuse that he was using an early form of calculus approximation!) Either way, this problem seems to have generated a similar amount of the substance that must have been deposited all over the Sicilian hills by Helios's vast herd of bulls.

Archimedes appears to have lived the normal eccentric life of a mathematician. Quiet, solitary, and quietly potty – with only the occasional spectacular incursion into the public arena (running naked through the streets shouting 'Eureka!', single-handedly launching Syracuse's forerunner to the *Titanic* etc). But at the end of his life events finally caught up with him, and he was forced once more to take a reluctant place on the public stage.

By the last decades of the third century BC the Mediterranean was in the grip of a power struggle between the two local superpowers – Rome expanding beyond the Italian mainland, and Carthage expanding beyond the shores of North Africa. In 218 BC this conflict erupted into the Second Punic War, with Hannibal leading his elephants across the Alps to attack Rome. Sicily was of vital strategic importance to both sides, and in 214 BC the Roman general Marcellus laid siege to Syracuse.

Archimedes was by now an old man in his 70s – a venerable age, in an era when people were lucky to survive their 30s. Despite this, he was placed in charge of the defence of Syracuse. The walls of the city ran sheer down to the sea, but nonetheless remained vulnerable to attack from the powerful Roman fleet. Archimedes personally supervised the military operations from these walls.

Using his scientific ingenuity to the full, he constructed a machine which hurled large stones at the enemy fleet. This would appear to have been some kind of catapult. He also constructed cranes which swung out from the walls and dropped large rocks that crashed through the decks of the Roman ships. He used a similar device to slide under the prows of the ships and hoist them out of the water.

The Roman commander Marcellus decided to storm the walls. He ordered his quinqueremes to be bound together, their masts strapped to either side of sambucas (wide scaling ladders which could be lowered against the walls). These then rowed hell for leather towards the city walls, their decks crammed with soldiers. Archimedes had apparently foreseen this, and used some kind of grappling device (again probably involving cranes) to dislodge the sambucas from the walls before the soldiers had time to scale them.

Most ingenious of all was a device made of many small flat mirrors which could focus the beams of the sun on a Roman ship. This device could operate 'at a distance of a bowshot', according to Plutarch, 'causing the air to become so dense that it ignited and set fire to the ships'. Plutarch's report is generally dismissed as fanciful. However, a suspiciously similar 'Archimedean machine' was said to have been used at the siege of Constantinople in 514 AD. In 1774 the French naturalist and constructor of eccentric machines, the Comte de Buffon, decided to test these reports. He built a concave dish containing 168 mirrors, which he found was capable of igniting wood at 50 metres, and at a shorter distance was even capable of melting lead.

The Roman commander Marcellus is said to have been greatly impresssed by the feats of his scientific adversary. So much so that when the city was finally overrun in 212 BC, he ordered that Archimedes' life should be spared. The ensuing story is almost as well known as the 'Eureka!' incident, and similarly varies according to source. The most dramatic account speaks of Archimedes deeply immersed in mathematical calculations as the Roman troops ransacked the city. Despite the mayhem in the streets outside, he continued drawing circles in his tray of smoothed sand (the contemporary equivalent of a personal computer). Archimedes was interrupted by a shadow falling across his drawings. He looked up and saw a Roman soldier. 'Please do not disturb my calculations,' he admonished the soldier. But the battle-weary soldier was evidently in no mood for a mathematical demonstration. Brandishing his sword he ordered Archimedes to accompany him; but Archimedes refused to budge until he had finished his calculations. Whereupon the exasperated Roman soldier struck him down, killing the obstinate old man.

This scene is depicted in a famous mosaic unearthed at Herculaneum, the city which was destroyed alongside Pompeii by Vesuvius in 79 AD. This mosaic can hardly be taken as an eyewitness report. (Reporters, even in Roman times, did not illustrate their reports with mosaics.) Yet it suggests that the legendary story of Archimedes' death may have had some basis in fact.

Marcellus was deeply upset when he heard what had happened to the 79-year-old mathematician – who was recognized, even then, as the finest scientific mind the world had yet seen. In recompense, Marcellus is said to have conferred honours on Archimedes' dependants, which suggests that he had probably been married. Marcellus also ordered that Archimedes' tombstone should be carved with a sphere inscribed within a cylinder, just as he had wished.

This last detail of the legend is factual. We know this from the writings of Cicero, the Roman orator and statesman. In 75 BC Cicero was appointed as Roman quaestor (paymaster general) of Sicily. He describes how one day he set off searching around the walls of Syracuse, looking for the reputed site of Archimedes' grave. In his own words: 'We eventually tracked down the graveyard. It was surrounded by a thicket of bushes and overgrown with brambles. I knew what to look for, as I had heard that on his tomb were written some lines of verse. I remembered these stated that a sphere and a cylinder had been inscribed on his tomb. There are a large number of graves at the Agrigentine Gate, and I had to search about for some time. Then I noticed a small column poking up above the bushes. On it I could just make out an inscription of a sphere and a cylinder. Slaves were sent ahead with scythes, and when they had cut a path through the undergrowth we approached the column. The inscribed verse was just traceable, with only half the lines still legible as the latter part was worn away.'

Apart from the famous mosaic, whose likeness is doubtful, the only known portrait of Archimedes is on a Sicilian coin dating from around the end of the third century BC. It is impossible to evaluate the likeness of this portrait. However, the portrait of Archimedes' mind which has come down to us in his writing is unmistakable. No one but a supreme mathematical genius could have created such works. This portrait of Archimedes will survive as long as mathematics itself.

AFTERWORD

At the time of Archimedes' death, Magna Graecia was falling to the Roman Empire. By the middle of the following century Rome had overrun Greece itself, and the great era of ancient Greek culture came to an end. Greek thinking was regarded as a mere ornament by the Roman Empire. It served no practical purpose. The Roman genius was for engineering, civic order and militarism. Their contribution to mathematics remains a blank. The only Roman to play a part in the history of mathematics was the soldier who slew Archimedes.

Archimedes' influence on subsequent generations was minimal. The enormity of his achievement was simply overlooked. Though his formulae, such as those for the surface area and volume of a sphere, became part of the standard mathematical canon. Likewise, his easily intelligible approximation of π as $^{22}\!/_{7}$ was also absorbed. This was correct to three decimal places – quite sufficient for the Romans. Although Archimedes had hoped that his 'mechanical method' (involving exhaustion, limits and so forth) would lead to new mathematical discoveries, this was not to be. Only when Archimedes' works were translated into Arabic in the eighth century did his hopes begin to be realized. Whilst Europe languished in intellectual darkness, it was the Arabs who finally restarted mathematics – which had lain dormant for a millennium.

Archimedes' works thus survived in one form or another into the Middle Ages and beyond. His practical ideas didn't appear to contradict Aristotelian orthodoxy, which meant they were acceptable to the medieval mind. Yet what did the medieval mind make of Archimedes' great theoretical works? Almost nothing, it seems. In Europe, mathematics continued to lie dormant. Or did it? A number of scholars remain convinced that *somewhere* in Europe *someone* must have seen Archimedes' work for what it was, and been inspired to make something further out of it. Mathematics needs no social tradition, it can as easily be practised by a lone monk in a remote island community as it can by a scholar in a university or a sage employed at a court. All that would have been needed were the works of Archimedes, and someone with sufficient intellect to use his method. A single solitary genius could easily have advanced mathematics on his own (and might then have passed on his works saving civilization from centuries of intellectual stagnation). Yet evidence of such a lost genius has yet to be found.

For the most part mathematics continued to be of use only as a practical tool. The human faculty for abstract mathematical thinking remained unused – except perhaps to calculate the amount of angels who could fit on a pinhead. The impulse to abstraction was diverted to fruitless theological speculation. This situation barely changed until the Renaissance. Not until the mid-16th century did Archimedes begin to inspire great minds – such as Kepler and Galileo. Even so, it was to be a century later before Newton advanced on Archimedes' method and created calculus. When asked how he had made his great discoveries, Newton famously replied: 'If I have seen further it is only by standing on the shoulders of giants.' But such modesty was only apparent. Newton was well aware that he was a giant, even among giants. And the only giant he recognized as his equal was Archimedes.

ARCHIMEDES AT WORK

Two of Archimedes' proofs:

On Floating Bodies, book 1 – Proposition 2
The surface of any fluid at rest is the surface of a sphere whose centre is the same as that of the earth.

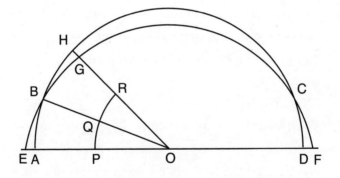

Suppose the surface of the fluid cut by a plane through O, the centre of the earth, in the curve ABCD.

ABCD shall be the circumference of a circle.

For, if not, some of the lines drawn from O to the curve will be unequal. Take one of them, OB, such that OB is greater than some of the lines from O to the curve and less than others. Draw a circle with OB as radius. Let it be EBF, which will therefore fall partly within and partly without the surface of the fluid.

Draw OGH making with OB an angle equal to the angle EOB, and meeting the surface in H and the circle in G. Draw also in the plane an arc of a circle PQR with centre O and within the fluid.

Then the parts of the fluid along PQR are uniform and continuous, and the part PQ is compressed by the part between it and AB, while the part QR is compressed by the part between QR and BH.

Therefore the parts along PQ, QR will be unequally compressed, and the part which is compressed the less will be set in motion by that which is compressed the more.

Therefore there will not be rest; which is contrary to the hypothesis.

Hence the section of the surface will be the

circumference of a circle whose centre is O; and so will all the other sections by planes through O.

Therefore the surface is that of a sphere with centre O.

Measurement of a Circle – Proposition 1
The area of any circle is equal to any right-angled triangle in which one of the sides about the right angle is equal to the radius, and the other to the circumference, of the circle.

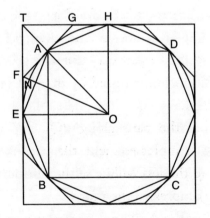

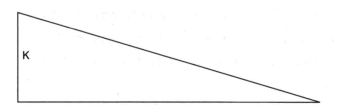

Let ABCD be the given circle, K the triangle described.

Then, if the circle is not equal to K, it must be either greater or less.

1. If possible, let the circle be greater than K.

Inscribe a square ABCD, bisect the arcs AB, BC, CD, DA, then bisect (if necessary) the halves, and so on, until the sides of the inscribed polygon whose angular points are the points of division subtend segments whose sum is less than the excess of the area of the circle over K.

Thus the area of the polygon is greater than K.

Let AE be any side of it, and ON the perpendicular on AE to the centre O.

Then ON is less than the radius of the circle and therefore less than one of the sides about the right angle in K. Also the perimeter of the polygon is less than the circumference of the circle ie, less than the other side about the right angle K.

Therefore the area of the polygon is less than K; which is inconsistent with the hypothesis.

Thus the area of the circle is not greater than K.

2. If possible, let the circle be less than K.

Circumscribe a square, and let two adjacent sides, touching the circle in E, H, meet in T. Bisect the arcs between adjacent points of contact and draw the tangents at the points of bisection. Let A be the middle point of the arc EH, and FAG the tangent at A.

Then the angle TAG is a right angle.

Therefore TG > GA

> GH

It follows that the triangle FTG is greater than half the area TEAH.

Similarly, if the arc AH be bisected and the tangent at the point of bisection be drawn, it will cut off from the area GAH more than one-half and so on.

Thus, by continuing the process, we shall ultimately arrive at a circumscribed polygon such that the spaces intercepted between it and the circle are together less than the excess of the area of the circle over K.

Thus the area of the polygon will be less than K.

Now, since the perpendicular from O on any side of the polygon is equal to the radius of the circle, while the perimeter of the polygon is greater than the circumference of the circle, it follows that the area of the polygon is greater than the triangle K; which is impossible.

Therefore the area of the circle is not less than K.

Since the area of the circle is neither greater than nor less than K, it is equal to it.

From this Archimedes goes on to prove that the circumference of a circle is equal to:

$\pi \times$ diameter

that the area of a circle is equal to:

$\pi \times (\text{radius})^2$

and that the value of π is:

$< 3\ \frac{1}{7}$ but $> 3\ \frac{10}{71}$

CHRONOLOGY OF ANCIENT GREEK ERA

1184 BC	Siege of Troy
776 BC	First Olympic Games
c700 BC	Age of Homer
585 BC	Solar eclipse predicted by Thales of Miletus, the first philosopher
545 BC	Persian Empire occupies Ionia (now Aegean coast of Turkish mainland)
533 BC	First competition for Greek Tragedy won by Thespis at Dionysia
490 BC	Persians defeated at Marathon
490 BC	Birth of Herodotus 'the father of history'
462 BC	Anaxagoras becomes first philosopher to live in Athens
460 BC	Start of First Peloponnesian War between Sparta and Athens. Birth

	of Hippocrates, leading Greek physician, responsible for the Hippocratic Oath
447 BC	Work starts on the Parthenon in Athens
429 BC	Death of Pericles marks end of Athens' golden era
427 BC	Birth of Plato
404 BC	Defeat of Athens by Sparta marks end of Peloponnesian Wars
399 BC	Socrates sentenced to death in Athens
329 BC	Alexander the Great reaches India
322 BC	Death of Aristotle
300 BC	Euclid writing in Alexandria
c290 BC	Founding of the Library at Alexandria
287 BC	Birth of Archimedes
264–241 BC	First Punic War between Rome and Carthage
218 BC	Second Punic War, with Hannibal invading Italy
212 BC	Death of Archimedes
211 BC	End of Second Punic War with

	Roman control of Sicily
168 BC	Roman defeat of Macedonia
146 BC	Sack of Corinth, Greece falls under Roman domination

SUGGESTIONS FOR FURTHER READING

E.J. Dijksterhuis: *Archimedes* (Munksgaard) – The best 'life and works', translated from the Dutch: occasionally reprinted, but remains rare.

E.T. Bell: *Men of Mathematics* (Longman) – The classic work on the subject; over 30 figures and their works from Ancient Greece to the start of the 20th century.

Euclid, Archimedes, Nicomachus: *Great Books of the Western World* Vol 10 (Britannica) – The complete works in the standard translation by Thomas L. Heath.

Cambridge Dictionary of Scientists (Cambridge) – Good on Archimedes' contemporaries; ideal for browsing.

David Wells: *The Penguin Dictionary of Curious and Interesting Numbers* (Penguin) – A sampler for addicts, a hook for beginners.

Also in the Big Idea *series . . .*

NEWTON & GRAVITY

Newton is one of the most influential scientists the world has ever known. Not only did he develop and formulate the theory of gravity, which gave mankind the first glimpse of the way the universe really worked, but he also discovered the concept of force, the nature of light, and changed the way we calculate. Newton's 'big ideas' were to transform the way we view the world forever.

Yet though we are all familiar with the theory of gravity (and the story of the apple falling from the tree), how many of us know how it really works? Newton's discoveries have so pervaded our everyday view that it is hard to understand how revolutionary his ideas really were. *Newton & Gravity* presents a brilliant snapshot of Newton's life and work, and gives a clear and accessible explanation of the meaning and importance of Newton's discoveries, and the way they have changed and influenced our own lives today.

EINSTEIN & RELATIVITY

$$E = mc^2$$

Few equations have entered our consciousness with the speed and impact of Einstein's cosmos-changing formula. From the moment in 1905 and 1917 he published his revolutionary papers on his Theory of Relativity, mankind's view of the world and the universe changed forever, the latest phase of the modern age was born, and our horizons shifted.

But how many of us really know what his theory really means, and what implications it has? *Einstein & Relativity* presents a brilliant snapshot of Einstein's life and work, together with their historical and scientific context, and gives a clear and accessible explanation of the meaning and importance of Einstein's Theory of Relativity, and the way it has changed and shaped our thinking in the twentieth century.

CRICK, WATSON & DNA

Francis Crick's and James Watson's discovery of DNA – the very building blocks of life – has astounding implications for mankind's future. Not only in the scientific possibilities of cloning, life expectancy and medical research, but also in our everyday lives – in the genetic engineering of food and in forensics, for example. The discovery of DNA has also raised important ethical questions.

But what is DNA? What gateways has its discovery opened for future generations? And what of the sometimes frantic race that the scientists Crick and Watson were engaged in against other scientists to understand its construction and open up a whole new field of science? *Crick, Watson & DNA* presents a brilliant snapshot of these two scientists' lives and work, and gives a clear and accessible explanation of the meaning and importance of the discovery of DNA, and its implications for the twentieth century and beyond.

TURING & THE COMPUTER

The computer has revolutionised the modern age of communication and information. It has touched every part of modern working life, to the extent that it would now be inconceivable without the computer. Its incredible power, and the speed it has brought to complex and multiple calculations, represent a massive leap forward in mankind's progress. Without doubt, the development of the computer is one of the twentieth century's greatest achievements.

But how many of us – even those of us who use a computer every day – know how it really works? And what of Alan Turing, the man who was a major figure in the development of the computer? The man who helped to break the Enigma codes during the Second World War, but who was largely forgotten after his death. *Turing & the Computer* presents a brilliant snapshot of Turing's life and work, and gives a clear and accessible explanation of the importance and meaning of the computer, and the way it has changed and shaped our lives in the twentieth century.

HAWKING & BLACK HOLES

Stephen Hawking is perhaps one of the best-known scientists of our day: his book *A Brief History of Time* is a world-wide bestseller. His discoveries and research on black holes and cosmology have been hailed as the next leap for mankind into new worlds and a new era. The possibilities may indeed be boundless. Hawking's 'big ideas' have changed the way we view the world and the cosmos, forever.

But despite their currency in today's popular fictions – novels, films, TV series – how many of us really understand what black holes are or might mean for future generations? *Hawking & Black Holes* presents a brilliant snapshot of Hawking's life and work, and gives a clear and accessible explanation of the meaning and importance of Hawking's discoveries, and the way they may change and influence our own lives today.

PYTHAGORAS & HIS THEOREM

$$a^2 + b^2 = c^2$$

Most of us have heard about Pythagoras through his theorem on right-angled triangles, having been taught that the square on the hypotenuse is equal to the sum of the squares on the other two sides. But many are unaware of the significance of his theorem and the equation that neatly sums this up, and the enormous implications this has had for the way we view the world today.

Pythagoras was arguably the first mathematician and philosopher in the Western world. His work changed the way people viewed the world, establishing concepts such as abstract reasoning and deductive proof. *Pythagoras & His Theorem* presents a brilliant snapshot of Pythagoras' life and work, putting them in their historical and scientific context, and gives a clear and accessible explanation of their meaning and significance for the world we live in today.

GALILEO & THE SOLAR SYSTEM

Galileo, who could have become the first great scientific martyr (but chose not to), was the Colossus who bridged the Renaissance of Leonardo and the Scientific Age of Newton. Without his discoveries mankind would have continued to be ignorant about the true nature of our solar system and our place in the universe. Galileo was the first person to describe the solar system as we know it, and through his development of the telescope, enabled others to share his vision.

We know that Galileo's findings were incredibly accurate, so why did he tell everyone that he was wrong? And why did he invent the thermometer when he was interested in space? *Galileo & the Solar System* presents a brilliant snapshot of Galileo, his controversial work and the historical background against which he was working. It gives a clear and accessible explanation of what Galileo's principles actually meant, and how they led to a scientific explanation of the universe for the twentieth century.

THE POWER OF READING

Visit the Random House website and get connected with information on all our books and authors

EXTRACTS from our recently published books and selected backlist titles

COMPETITIONS AND PRIZE DRAWS Win signed books, audiobooks and more

AUTHOR EVENTS Find out which of our authors are on tour and where you can meet them

LATEST NEWS on bestsellers, awards and new publications

MINISITES with exclusive special features dedicated to our authors and their titles

READING GROUPS Reading guides, special features and all the information you need for your reading group

LISTEN to extracts from the latest audiobook publications

WATCH video clips of interviews and readings with our authors

RANDOM HOUSE INFORMATION including advice for writers, job vacancies and all your general queries answered

Come home to Random House

www.rbooks.co.uk